BHARTI VYAS

TWO DAY TREAT

I dedicate this book to my beloved husband, Raja, who has always given me the freedom to follow my path in life. He, along with my daughters, Shailu and Priti, have given me unconditional love, support, encouragement and belief. Without them I would be nowhere. I also dedicate this book to my dear late mother, Pushpaben, and to my aunt, Vijyaben, who has been a second mother to me. They were both an inspiration to me for, as Indian women, they were both far ahead of their era. And to my grandchildren, who have always inspired me to carry on.

BHARTI VYAS

TWO DAY TREAT

PERFECT WELLBEING IN A WEEKEND

Thorsons

Thorsons
An Imprint of HarperCollins*Publishers*
77–85 Fulham Palace Road,
Hammersmith, London W6 8JB

The Thorsons website address is: www.thorsons.com

Extracts taken from *Beauty Wisdom* and *Simply Radiant,*
published by Thorsons 1997, 1999.
This edition published by Thorsons, 2000

1 3 5 7 9 10 8 6 4 2

© Bharti Vyas 2000

Bharti Vyas, Jane Warren and Clare Haggard assert the moral right to
be identified as the authors of this work

A catalogue record for this book
is available from the British Library

ISBN 0 7225 4012 4

Printed and bound in Great Britain by
Woolnough Bookbinding Ltd, Irthingborough, Northamptonshire

CONTENTS

Introduction

Welcome to Your Spa Weekend

There is a fundamental truth about beauty care: *beauty on the outside begins on the inside.* I hope that, in this book, I can help you start to make the connection between your inner health and outer beauty, between inner vitality and outer radiance.

By taking a weekend out to try the routines I give you, you will begin to see improvements in your appearance, health and wellbeing. And, if you go on to make these routines a way of life, you will develop new found confidence in your looks and discover stores of untapped energy.

Remember, if you *know* you look good, you can take on the world!

BHARTI VYAS

Friday evening

Friday evening is often an ideal time to relax and let go of the stresses of the week. I often hear women saying that they do not have time to relax because they are too busy. It is exactly such women who most need the benefits proper relaxation can bring. Relaxing is one of the most effective ways of counteracting stress. It diffuses the accumulated physical and psychological pressure so that, when you go back into battle, you feel refreshed and your load feels lighter.

One of the most therapeutic treatments we can give ourselves is a long, relaxing soak in the bath.

BATHTIME WITH BHARTI

First prepare everything you are going to need – your cassette player if you want to listen to music, a good book or magazine, and a towel to dry your hands.

Make sure you have a flannel available and a large towel to cover the floor. The room needs to be comfortably warm. Light some candles around the bath to evoke atmosphere; the gently flickering light will help your body unwind.

ALL-PURPOSE OATMEAL POLISHER

2 tbs finely ground oatmeal
1 tbs almond oil

Combine ingredients, apply to skin and rub with a very light action using the balls of your fingers, then rinse off. Do not apply sustained pressure to any particular spot.

BODY POLISHING

Stand on the floor and rub the *All-purpose Oatmeal Polisher* into your skin, first over your trunk, then onto your arms, legs, neck, face and even behind your ears. This is very invigorating and you will notice your skin becoming warm and pink in response. Pay special attention to the hard skin on your elbows, knees, soles and heels, on which the polish has a remarkable softening effect. Massage the paste into finger and toenails, working right into the cuticles. Shower the paste off.

I believe passionately in the benefits of liquid mineral salts. The very high concentration of minerals in the salts, tiny quantities of which enter the body through the pores, have a natural therapeutic action on the skin and benefit the body as a whole. Their effect on the external body is to boost the skin's excretory function by dissolving the dehydrated cells that accumulate on the surface. This speeds up the elimination of the body's waste and has a smoothing effect on the skin.

THE MAGIC OF MINERALS

Now fill up the bath and add three or four capfuls of liquid mineral salts plus a squirt of bath and shower gel for your mineral therapy. If you suffer from a dry skin condition such as eczema, start with as little as a capful of liquid mineral salts, increasing gradually as tolerance builds up. If your skin is raw or cracked you will feel a mild burning sensation. Do not worry – remember: Salts are healing.

The water should be pleasantly warm, so that you feel inclined to linger. If the bath is too hot, it will stimulate rather than relax your system and can also have a dehydrating and slackening effect on the skin, as well as damaging fragile capillaries.

Submerge yourself in the bath for 20 minutes.

FINISHING UP

Shower yourself and apply a good body lotion to further hydrate the skin.

Now go straight to bed and let the therapy go on working overnight.

Saturday morning

9 am

BREAKFAST

One cup of Chai
Two pieces of brown bread with a
small amount of butter

Chai is tea, usually made in a *samovar*, it is part of the way most Indians start their day. We like our tea sweetened with a little sugar, and pungent with spices, especially cinnamon and nutmeg. Busy people rarely have time for the luxury of a samovar, but you can buy some excellent blends of Indian spiced tea in any supermarket.

To make at home, rinse out a tea pot with boiling water to warm it, and add enough black tea to make two or three cups. Add a small piece of cinnamon (about an inch), a few cardamom pods, several whole cloves, about $1/4$ teaspoon of freshly ground nutmeg and two teaspoons of sugar. Pour in the boiling water and allow the mixture to brew for about five minutes. Now add two or three tablespoons of milk. Stir. The milk helps bind the tannin from the tea, making it more digestible than tea with lemon. Strain and enjoy.

HAIR AND SCALP

Our hair has the power to lift or depress our spirits. Beautiful hair is as much a source of pride for a man as it is for a woman and we spend millions of pounds teasing and taming our crowning glory in an attempt to make the most of what we have. Yet the real secret lies in understanding how to nurture our hair and improve its condition from the *inside*.

THE SCALP

- The most effective way to keep your scalp in working order is to massage it regularly with oil.
- A scalp massage is a wonderful therapy for mind and body, capable of clearing your head, lifting your spirits and evaporating tension, at the same time as looking after one of your best assets. See *The Bharti Vyas Scalp Massage* opposite.
- When blow-drying do not use an appliance over 1200 watts and work with a diffuser attachment to spread the heat. Always keep the dryer moving, at a distance of about six inches from the hair.
- Dry in the following order: back, side, crown, then front.
- Allow your hair to dry naturally as often as possible, using your hands to create shape and lift the roots.

THE BHARTI VYAS SCALP MASSAGE

Measure out three tablespoons of liquefied coconut oil. Halve the quantity if your hair is oily or very fine. Begin by activating acupressure point *Governing Vessel 20* (see page 17).

Dip a cotton wool ball into the oil and squeeze it so that it's not dripping. Apply to your scalp along the hair parting.

Continue to part your hair at regular intervals across the front of your head until you reach the tips of your ears, rubbing oil onto the scalp as you go.

Replenish the cotton wool with oil as needed and repeat the process at the back of your head until every inch of your scalp is covered lightly.

Now use the balls of your fingers to manipulate your scalp and help loosen it. Apply as much pressure as is comfortable, going easily over tender spots. Most people find that they need to start very gently, pressing lightly with the fingers, progressively increasing the pressure so that the fingers are really working the scalp. Don't give up if it seems totally unyielding to begin with, it may take a few weeks before your scalp really starts to relax.

Pay proper attention to the section at the base of the skull – which can become very tight – by circling your thumbs along the hairline with your fingers resting on the back of your head. Pour any remaining oil onto the central parting and rub vigorously. Run your fingers through your hair to disperse the oil. When you have completed the scalp massage, wrap your hair in a towel or shower cap.

Like the skin, the hair has a natural coating of oil, produced in the follicles, which is of a slightly acidic nature. The one guiding principle when it comes to washing, treating and styling your hair is to avoid stripping it of this 'acid mantle'.

Hair Washing

Hair really needs washing only when it loses its 'bounce' and starts to look dull and lifeless. However, if your hair is oily or very fine, or you suffer from dandruff or psoriasis, you may not feel confident unless you give it a daily wash. Once your scalp is in peak condition, twice a week should be more than adequate.

(If you have eczema or psoriasis try oiling your scalp every evening.)

De-tangle your hair before you wash it as wet hair is extremely fragile.

Use a gentle, pH-balanced shampoo to preserve the acid mantle.

ACUPRESSURE WORKS WONDERS

Acupressure is another way of using our hands to enhance our health and vitality. According to Chinese medicine, the energy or vital force inhabiting every individual flows along established channels or meridians. These are connected to the organs and systems of the body. When this flow of energy is interrupted, it creates an imbalance in the body which is manifested on the outside as a problem or a symptom. By stimulating the pressure points of the meridians which lie just beneath the surface of the skin (acupressure points or acupoints), the natural harmony can be restored.

Governing Vessel 20 (GV 20)

Location: in the middle of the head, halfway between the ears. Position thumbs on the tips of the ears, to get your bearings, then apply gentle pressure using your middle finger.

Benefits: this is the most powerful sedative point in the body. Balances emotions and sharpens mental faculties, as well as improving memory and powers of concentration. Very effective in regulating blood pressure and raising general energy levels.

Extra Point 6

Location: two finger widths above, below and to the left and right of GV 20. Apply pressure with the first and second finger of each hand.

Benefits: relieves anxiety and insomnia and balances the mind and emotions.

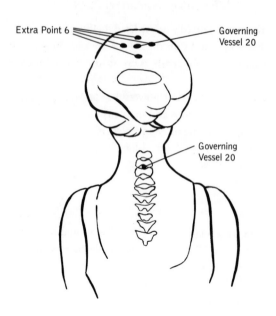

Extra Point 6

Governing Vessel 20

Governing Vessel 20

MORNING EXERCISE

Good muscle tone is important for our health and our looks. Muscle tone is what keeps the fleshy part of our muscles firm and effectual. When tone is lost, the muscle becomes less efficient and wastes accumulate.

FACIAL EXERCISE — THE LION POSE

Do the following exercise to stop your face and neck losing tone.

- ◉ Take a deep breath and, as you breathe out slowly, open your mouth as wide as possible and stick your tongue out as far as it will go. At the same time, look at the ceiling without raising your head or straining your eyes.
- ◉ Maintain the position and count slowly up to 12. Aim for five repetitions.

Elsewhere in the body it is generally the large muscles which give us trouble — the buttocks, fronts and backs of thighs, abdominal muscles and upper arms — as when they are slack and out-of-condition, they have a powerful attraction for fat, fluid and toxins.

Put on some comfortable clothes and shoes and go for a walk for half an hour.

Walking keeps your calf and thigh muscles active, and helps the difficult task of pumping your blood and lymph back up the legs against gravity.

Be conscious at every step of your upper and lower leg muscles working all the time. Land on your heel and spring from one foot to the other. Take off from the balls of your feet and squeeze your buttock muscles to propel yourself forward.

Now you are warm find a spacious area to try some of these simple toning exercises:

Bust

◉ Stretch your arms out in front of you, bend them at the elbow and grasp each forearm firmly below the elbow with the opposite hand.

◉ Breathe in slowly through the nose and, as you breathe out, tighten your grip and hold for a count of five, increasing to 10. Repeat 10 times.

Stomach

For your abdominal 'corset' to hold you firmly in place, all four of the superficial abdominal muscles need to be worked.

- This is the yoga posture known as *Uddiyana Bandha*. Standing comfortably with your legs apart, bend your body forward and rest your hands on your thighs. Allow your chin to drop towards your chest and breathe in.
- Now breathe out and, as you get to the end of the breath, pull your abdominal muscles upwards and backwards towards your chest.
- Do this in stages until you have scooped up every last bit of muscle and hold for as long as you can. You may only be able to manage once or twice, but, if you continue to practise this exercise after the weekend, aim in the long run for five repetitions.
- Stand with your hands hanging loosely by your sides and your legs shoulder width apart. Twist and rotate

your trunk at your waist, so that you are now looking over your right shoulder.

- ✦ Repeat 10 times on each side, edging further round as you loosen up. Breathe slowly and deeply throughout.

Buttocks

You will be amazed at the toning effect of regular buttock-clenching. Get into the habit of tightening your buttocks, whether standing or sitting, every time you think of it:

◉ Stand with the pelvis well-balanced and the upper body relaxed. Now really squeeze the buttocks, so that the cheeks are pulled together. This will tighten up muscle tone and help release stored toxins. Your stomach muscles should benefit too, as they are automatically pulled in at the same time.

Thighs

- Use the plié, a classic ballet posture, to work the muscles of the thighs. Place your hands on your hips and stand with your heels together and your toes pointing outwards. Breathe in and rise up onto your toes. Breathe out and lower yourself into a squatting position, making sure that your back is straight. Do not go any lower than is comfortable. Breathe in again and pressing on the balls of your feet, raise yourself as slowly as you can to the standing position. Breathe out and rest. Repeat three times.

- Sit with your back up against a firm surface, your knees bent and your fingertips resting on the floor beside you. Place a cushion between your knees, breathe in and, as you breathe out, squeeze the cushion between your inner thighs for a slow count of eight. Repeat five times. Make sure your inner thighs are doing the work while other parts of your legs are relaxed.

NUTRITION

If you want a healthy body, you must first have a healthy and balanced diet.

The food we eat provides us with the energy we need to live and the raw materials for the growth, maintenance and repair of our bodies. A regular intake of the essential vitamins, minerals, fibre, fats, carbohydrates and protein, together with water – in other words, a balanced diet – is all that it takes to keep the body's complex machinery ticking over. By supplying our bodies with these nutrients, we are also providing our skin, nails, hair, teeth, muscles and bones with the first class nourishment they require. Poor eating habits and digestive problems undermine our general health and increase our susceptibility to illness. In a relatively short time, they can also have a visible impact on our appearance – most noticeably on the condition of our, hair, nails and skin.

BHARTI'S 'BREAD'

First start by preparing my special 'bread'. This is a slimming food full of flavour which you can keep throughout the weekend.

(serves 4)

Ingredients

2 tbsp corn oil

1 tbsp black mustard seeds

1^1/2 tsp sea salt

^{1}/2 tsp freshly ground black pepper

1 small chilli, seeded and chopped

1 large onion, chopped

1 large red pepper, seeded and chopped

140g/5oz/1 cup gram flour

240ml/8fl oz/1 cup soya milk (unsweetened)

3 medium eggs, beaten

225g/8oz/1 cup Quark, or other very low-fat cheese

1 tbsp garam masala (or commercial curry powder)

Low-fat cheese is a good source of calcium, which benefits teeth and bones, nerve and muscle health, and promotes normal blood clotting.

Gram flour, made from chickpeas (garbanzo beans), is a good source of manganese, which is also needed for healthy bones and skin. It also contains folate, iron and vitamin E. It is widely used in Indian cookery.

1 Preheat the oven to 175ºC/325ºF/Gas 3. Butter a 23cm (9 in) square baking pan or lasagne dish.

2 Combine the oil, mustard seeds, salt, black pepper and chilli in a heavy frying pan and heat until the seeds 'pop'. Add the onion and red pepper, cover and cook until the vegetables are tender.

3 Meanwhile, combine the gram flour and soya milk in a large mixing bowl. Add the eggs gradually. (Gram flour is surprisingly heavy, so the mixture will be thick.)

4 Add the low-fat cheese and mix well to combine. Stir in the cooked vegetables, spices and oil and the garam masala.

5 Pour the mixture into the prepared dish and bake for 30 minutes, or until the centre of the 'bread' is firm.

LENTIL SOUP WITH SUN-DRIED TOMATOES

(Serves 2)

Ingredients

115g/4oz/^{1}/$_2$ cup of split red lentils
About a litre/35fl oz/4^1/$_2$ cups water
4 tbsp virgin olive oil
1 small onion, finely chopped
1 large garlic clove, minced
1 tsp black mustard seed
1 small, dried chilli pepper, crushed
1 bay leaf
^{1}/$_2$ tsp ground cloves
1 tsp ground cumin
4–5 sun-dried tomatoes, cut into small pieces
1 stock (bouillon) cube
(vegetarian or chicken), crumbled
salt and black pepper to taste

1 Place the lentils in a large pot or bowl, add the water and allow to soak for at least 15 minutes.

2 Pour the oil into a heavy soup pot over a medium heat. Add the onion, garlic, mustard seed and chilli, and stir. Turn the heat down as low as possible, cover the pan and allow to 'sweat'; after 6 or 7 minutes, check to see that the vegetables are cooking, but not burning. Remove from the heat.

3 Carefully add the lentils and water to the mixture of vegetables and oil. Add the bay leaf, cloves and cumin. Place over medium heat and bring to the boil. Cook for five minutes, turn the heat to low, cover and simmer for 30 minutes, stirring once or twice to stop the lentils from sticking.

4 Add the sun-dried tomato pieces (remove excess oil) and stock (bouillon) cube. Replace the lid and simmer for another half-hour, stirring occasionally. Add more water if necessary.

5 Remove the bay leaf from the soup. Season to taste.

Mustard seeds are an ancient remedy for headache and flu. Black mustard is hotter than brown.

Lentils are a good source of slow-release energy. As they are life-bearing foods, they contain important B vitamins, minerals and fats, which your body needs for health.

1.30pm

LUNCH

Bharti 'Bread' and Lentil and Sun-dried Tomato soup

DEEP CLEANSE

Try not to allow wheat and dairy products to dominate your diet. Gluten, the gummy protein in wheat, and mucus-forming milk, cream, cheese and butter have a tendency to clog up the intestines and interfere with nutrient absorption. Tell-tale signs of congestion include a general feeling of sluggishness and an increase in the frequency of colds and mucus conditions. There is often expansion around the midriff too, not accompanied by weight gain elsewhere.

Your weekend menu will give you a chance to enjoy a diet free from wheat and low in dairy products.

Wheat Products	Wheat Alternatives
Bread	100 per cent rye bread and crispbread
Pasta	Rice (grains, cakes, noodles)
Most cakes and biscuits	Potatoes
Many breakfast cereals	Oats (oatcakes, porridge, oatbran)
Semolina, Couscous, Bulgar	Corn (polenta, tortillas, cornflakes)
Wheatgerm and bran	Popcorn, corn chips
Wheat flour	Cornflour, potato flour, arrowroot

Dairy Products	*Dairy Alternatives*
Milk	Goat's milk/cheese/yogurt
Butter	Sheep's milk/cheese/yogurt
Some margarines	Soya milk/yogurt, tofu
Cheese	Mayonnaise
Yogurt	Cold-pressed oils
	Tahini
	Hummus

Saturday afternoon

PAMPER YOURSELF WITH
A HOME FACIAL

Beautiful skin rests on three essential pillars:

- Cleansing
- Moisturizing
- Skin Polishing

CLEANSING

It may seem an obvious point, but keeping your skin clean is the number one skincare priority. Cleanse you face both morning and night: in the morning to remove surface oil and dead skin cells after the night-time repair work to the skin has taken place, so that you begin the day with fresh skin; in the evening to remove grime which has accumulated during the day and all traces of make-up. The morning need be no more than a swipe with a damp face cloth, but the evening cleanse should be extremely thorough. **Remember:** for cleansing purposes, your face starts at your collarbones and stops at your hairline.

Washing with the right soap is one of the most effective ways of removing dirt and bacteria from your skin. Although most parts of your body do not require soap to get them clean, it is important to use soap in the areas of the body where sweat is prone to become trapped. People are frightened of using soap on their faces but, provided your skin is healthy and you moisturize properly, there is no reason to avoid it. The harm is done by harsh – that is, very alkaline – soaps which disturb the skin's acid mantle.

One of the oldest — and gentlest — methods of cleansing the skin, which cuts through surface grime and stale make-up without stripping the skin of its protective film, is *oil*. I am a particular fan of almond oil, but an unrefined vegetable oil, such as sunflower, is equally good. For sensitive and acne-prone skin it is a useful way to remove dead cells without irritation. I unreservedly recommend oil for mature skins.

Apply a light film of oil all over your neck and face, including your eyelids, and rub in gently using the balls of your fingers. Leave for up to a minute to allow it to work and remove with a dampened cotton wool or facial sponge.

POLISHING YOUR SKIN

For our skin to remain clear, smooth and translucent, the surface layer needs to be free of any superfluous cells and its excretory activities able to continue unimpeded.

Use one of the home therapies opposite.

GENTLE FACIAL POLISHER

(Sensitive Skin)

2 heaped tsp fine oatmeal
2 tsp double cream

Combine ingredients, apply to skin and rub with very light action using the balls of your fingers, then rinse off. Do not apply sustained pressure to any particular spot.

POLISHER

(Irregular Pigmentation)

2 heaped tsp fine oatmeal
2 tsp honey
$1/4$ tsp lemon consistency

Sloppy consistency. Leave on for 10 minutes.

SOOTHING

FACE MASKS

Apply one of these masks to your skin and leave for the specified amount of time.

CLEANSING MASK

2 heaped tsp gram (chickpea) flour
1 tsp honey
1 tsp water

Thick, sticky consistency. Apply to affected areas and leave for five to seven minutes.

HEALING MASK

2 tsp honey
$1/4$ tsp fine sea salt
1 tsp turmeric

Thick paste. Apply to spots and leave on for up to 30 minutes.

STABILIZING FACE MASK

(Sensitive Skin, Acne Rosacea, Premature Wrinkles)

1 heaped tsp gram (chickpea) flour
1 tsp double cream
2 tsp water and a pinch of salt

A thick and creamy consistency. Apply to skin and leave for 10 minutes before rinsing off.

FIRMING MASK

2 heaped tsp gram (chickpea) flour
2 tsp water
$1/2$ tsp honey

Creamy paste. Leave on for 15 minutes.

You can also try these masks for the nose and eyes:

NOSE MASK

$^1/_2$ tsp gram (chickpea) flour
$^1/_2$ tsp honey
a pinch of salt
a few drops of lemon juice

Cover your nose with the paste, allowing it to overlap onto your cheeks. Leave for five to 10 minutes.

EYE MASK

2 tsp juice grated cucumber
1 tsp powdered milk

Thick paste. Close eyes and cover upper and lower eyelids. Leave for 10 minutes then wipe off with moist cotton wool.

SUNCARE

Now that you have cleansed and healed your skin apply a good moisturizer.

Sunscreens are incorporated into many cosmetics nowadays, so there is no excuse not to use a sunscreen all year round. For those serious about preserving the fragile skin on their face and neck, there is no better insurance policy than an application of SPF 15 every day of the year. Antioxidant vitamins A, C and E – either in tablet form or applied to your face at night in an oil or cosmetic cream formulation – will further limit the free-radical damage.

FACIAL MASSAGE

Self-massage is an invaluable beauty tool. Massage not only tones the muscles and relieves congestion, but promotes relaxation and internal balance. Facial and neck massage is a great way to delay the signs of ageing.

First you need to learn my four simple massage techniques.

BHARTI'S FOUR MASSAGE TECHNIQUES:

Pinching (for face & body)

Use tiny pinches with the thumb and index finger in small areas like the temple. For larger areas such as the shoulder, pinch with the thumb and four fingers. Pinching is a fast action which activates the skin's nerve endings and revives cells, helping to drain away waste via the lymph.

Palming (for face & body)

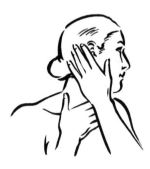

A light, stroking action with the palms corrects imbalances in different parts of the body and can be more effective than a deep massage. The palms radiate heat and have a powerful, magnetic healing action.

Finger Balls (for scalp, face & body)

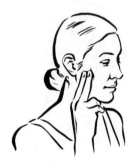

Using a series of small, circular movements you stimulate the nerve endings and activate blood vessels and the lymphatic system. The balls of your fingers are highly sensitive.

Feather Massage (for face & body)

Use the fingers to create light, feathery upward strokes to stimulate the para-sympathetic nervous system. This particularly is suitable for those with a low pain threshold, very sensitive skin or for using upon parts of the body that are swollen.

NOTE: Do not massage the site of an open wound or areas where the skin is sore or infected.

Smoking reduces the level of vitamin C available to the body essential for healthy collagen, as well as interfering with the supply of oxygen to the cells. An inadequate supply of protein in the diet will also adversely affect the production of new collagen and so, like smoking, lead to an increased tendency to premature lines and wrinkles.

Before beginning make sure that your hair is well back off your face and that you have removed any jewellery. Remove your bra or pull your straps down. Pour a few tablespoons of your massage oil into a bowl and apply a light film all over your face and neck.

Look on page 88 for recommendations of which oils to use.

THE NECK

We have to be very careful in our treatment of our neck due to the delicate nature of the tissue, the underlying thyroid gland and the proximity of the voicebox. This routine uses the magnetic field of the palms to influence the metabolism via the thyroid and adjoining parathyroid glands, as well as keeping the skin firm and supple.

Massage the neck from left to right in a rhythmical, upward-stroking movement, with one hand following the other. If you start with the palms at the base of your neck, you should finish with your forefingers up under the chin.

Continue for two or three minutes.

Next, pinch gently all over the front and sides of your neck for a further minute. Use your right hand for the left side and vice versa. Finish with an additional two minutes of stroking.

JAWLINE

Position your thumbs just beneath your chin and the balls of your fingers on the top. Now pinch your way along the lower jawbone until you reach the earlobes, applying greater pressure at the corner of the jawbone and just beneath the earlobes. You should work deeply enough to feel the jawbone. Aim to cover the distance in four pinches, repeat the sequence 10 times.

CHEEKS

Using the first two fingers of each hand, work along the underside of the cheekbones, pressing the balls of your fingers gently against and then releasing them. Work out towards the point where your cheekbones and upper jawbones meet, then come back towards the centre, four or five moves in each direction. Repeat 10 times.

SINUS POINTS

This exercise will help to clear or prevent blocked sinuses. Once you clear the sinus points you will automatically feel and look better as well as regaining your sense of smell.

Using the balls of your index fingers, apply pressure to the muscles on either side of the nose, starting at the bridge and moving to the nostrils. Your fingers should be pointing inwards so that you feel cartilage rather than bone.

EYES

The skin around the eyes is the thinnest anywhere in the body and one of the first places on our face to show signs of ageing. In addition to keeping it moisturized, the following routine will help to avoid stagnation in the tissue by stimulating the lymphatic drainage.

Close your eyes and feel the bony rims of your eye sockets. Starting at the outer edge, use your third fingers to trace around the rims of the sockets, applying more pressure across your brow at the point where the eyebrow meets the side of the nose.

Do at least 10 laps at a steady pace, working both eyes simultaneously. Only use your third fingers, as this will prevent you from exerting too much pressure on the delicate eye tissue.

FOREHEAD

Position your thumbs just above the outer edge of your eyebrows and your index fingers above the inner edge. Pinch in a rhythmical fashion up towards the hairline and back again. Now place your thumbs on your temples and repeat.

Continue this for a couple of minutes.

Although this is a very shallow pinch – almost a flick, as there is so little flesh to get hold of – it is effective in encouraging regeneration and preventing lines.

Taiyang

Location: one thumb width beyond the eyebrow, in a dip in the skin halfway between the outer edge of the eyebrow and the corner of the eye. Apply circular pressure using your finger for about a minute.

Benefits: relaxes tense facial muscles, revitalizes expression and smoothe complexion.

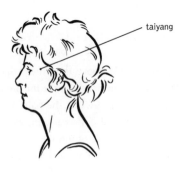

taiyang

TIDY UP YOUR EYEBROWS

Some people are lucky enough to be born with shapely, tidy eyebrows. Most of us, however, have our work cut out. Here are a few practical tips which may make the task a little easier.

- The most natural and flattering eyebrow shape is an arc with its highest point above the outside of the iris. Start by removing hairs from the inner edge and the bridge of the nose.
- Now prune the centre and outer edge, allowing the line to taper gradually to nothing. To find out where the brow should end, imagine a line connecting the outside of your nostril with the outer corner of your eye and extending out to your brow.
- Finally, pull out any stray hairs below the brows. The less you pluck, the easier it is to maintain the shape. Over-plucking may leave you with permanently sparse brows.

LOOK AFTER YOUR
MOUTH

The mouth is the most sensual feature on our face, both from the point of view of appearance and the sensations it enables us to experience.

Our lips are covered on the outside by a thin layer of skin and on the inside by virtually transparent mucous membranes and are very easily damaged. Unlike most of the skin on the body, they do not have melanin to protect them. A sunscreen in summer and barrier screen in winter are therefore vital.

MOUTH EXERCISES

⊛ Twitching your nose is an effective way of mobilizing the muscles in the middle of the face and helping to prevent lines on the upper lip.

⊛ The idea is to make up small up and down movements without creating too many creases over the bridge. If you practise while looking in a mirror, you will see how it activates the cheek area and the skin between the nose and mouth.

⊛ Now, try the second exercise. Close your mouth and inflate the skin above the upper lip and on either side of the mouth, while you continue to breathe through your nose.

⊛ Hold for a count of 10, and then repeat 10 times.

⊛ You must keep your upper lip smooth and relaxed throughout – it may help to position one finger above each corner of your mouth and hold the skin in place.

Almond oil applied to your lips and the skin around the mouth will help to keep the area supple.

LOOKING AFTER YOUR TEETH

The importance of oral hygiene cannot be overemphasized. Unless you protect your teeth and gums with regular and effective brushing and flossing, you are inviting decay and gum disease.

The purpose of cleaning is to remove the destructive plaque that settles on the surface of the teeth and the spaces between them. If not removed it produces acids, which dissolve the enamel and attack the gums and eventually hardens to form unsightly yellow tartar. Plaque is also an underlying cause of bad breath and stained teeth.

What to do

- Book a dental check-up.
- Make sure you are using toothpaste that contains fluoride.
- Brush your teeth *and* gums.
- Floss between your teeth.
- To build and maintain strong teeth you need an adequate supply of calcium and vitamins C and D.
- Avoid sugary sweets or starchy foods that cause decay. Brush too after eating dried fruits and unsweetened fruit juices.
- To whiten teeth, use bicarbonate of soda on a damp toothbrush and polish until they gleam.
- The Indian habit of chewing fennel and cardamom seeds after meals helps to prevent tooth decay, gum disease and associated bad breath. Chomping on a handful of parsley is a tried and tested method of removing the smell of garlic and other strong-smelling food on the breath.

Lemon juice is a great cleanser and healer with anti-bacterial properties. It is also a useful bleaching agent and from an early age can be rubbed onto skin to prevent hair growth. Try this mask for excess hair:

LEMON MASK

1 tsp lemon juice
1 tsp honey

A very liquid mask; smooth the paste on in the direction of hair growth and leave for 10 minutes.

Saturday evening

7.30pm

DINNER

Enjoy your evening meal of:

Gingered Beans and Tomato
Bharti's Special Dal
Plain Rice
Spicy Mango

GINGERED BEANS WITH TOMATO

(Serves 4)

Ingredients

1 can/425g/14oz chopped plum tomatoes
1 small onion, chopped
130g/4^{1}/2oz/1^{1}/2 cup frozen (fava) beans
(peas or French beans may be substituted)
1 stock (bouillon) cube
(vegetable or chicken), crumbled
1 tbsp ground ginger
1 tsp sugar
salt and black pepper to taste
1 tbsp ghee, or butter

1 Combine tomatoes, onion, beans and stock (bouillon) cube in a heavy pan; cover and cook over low heat until vegetables are soft. Remove the lid, turn up heat, and watching carefully, cook the mixture until most of the liquid has evaporated.

2 Add the ginger, sugar and a few 'turns' of freshly ground pepper.

3 Stir in the ghee, or butter. Adjust the salt and pepper to taste, and serve with plain rice and dal.

Ginger is a highly therapeutic food. It helps calm the digestion, prevent motion sickness and nausea, and stimulate circulation of the blood.

BHARTI'S SPECIAL DAL

(serves 4)

Ingredients

1 can/425g/14oz cooked chickpeas (garbanzo beans)
1 can/425g/14oz cooked soya beans (soy beans)
squeeze of lemon juice
3 tbsp corn oil or ghee
1 tsp cumin seeds
1 tsp ground coriander
1 large onion, finely chopped
1 large red pepper, seeded and chopped
1 tsp finely chopped fresh root ginger
2 large garlic cloves, minced
1 large green chilli, seeded and finely chopped
black pepper from 6 to 8 turns of large pepper mill
1 tsp salt

1 Empty both cans of beans into a large sieve and rinse well under cold running water. Tap dry and, with the beans still in the sieve, top with the lemon juice and gently shake to distribute the juice.

2 Place the oil, or ghee, and all the spices in a heavy pan. Add the onion, pepper, ginger, garlic and chilli, and cook until the onions are translucent. Remove the pan from the heat.

3 In a separate pan, combine the beans with 3 or 4 tablespoons of water and bring to the boil. Turn down the heat to a simmer, cover the pan tightly and mash the beans well.

4 Add the cooked ingredients to the beans and mash again. Season to taste and serve.

Soya is one of the most powerful foods we can eat to protect our health and slow the advance of signs of age. Substances called *isoflavones*, which are similar to the body's natural oestrogen, are believed to help maintain smooth skin and strong bones, and prevent certain forms of cancer. Extensive laboratory research done around the world suggests that genistein, protease inhibitors and phytic acids – all compounds found in soya – stop the formation of cancer in its early stages, or actually kill cancer cells.

I use a standard measuring cup to measure my rice, because it is by far the simplest and quickest way, but if you do not have one, measure out 450ml (15fl oz) of rice in a normal measuring cup.

(Serves 6)

Ingredients

2 cups of long-grain rice (Basmati is best)
1 litre/35fl oz/4$\frac{1}{2}$ cups of water

1 Wash the rice several times, cover with water and allow to stand for at least 15 minutes.
2 Drain the rice and place in a heavy pan with a tight-fitting lid. Add the water. Place the uncovered pan over a high heat and bring to the boil.
3 Turn the heat to very low. Cover the pan and cook for 25 minutes.
4 Remove the pan from the heat. Do not remove the lid. Leave to cool for at least 10 minutes.

WONDERFUL WATER

Nearly two-thirds of our body weight is made up of water. We need water to aid our digestion and elimination. When we don't take in enough, toxins get trapped in our tissues, causing the complexion to deteriorate and laying the foundations for cellulite and the degeneration that heralds the start of the ageing process. So drink eight to 10 glasses of water per day, ideally still-bottled or filtered.

SPICY MANGO

Try this easy dessert after your Saturday evening meal.

Peel and slice a ripe mango. Place the slices in a sauté pan containing a little melted butter. Warm the slices on one side, then turn and warm the other. The flesh should just begin to brown at the edges. Remove the fruit to dessert plates and sprinkle with ground ginger and salt. A definite success.

Mangoes are rich in betacarotene, a substance the body makes into vitamin A, which is important for healthy skin and essential for a strong immune system. However, on its own betacarotene is a powerful nutrient, more potent in some ways than vitamin A. Studies suggest it helps fight cancers of the bladder, breast and cervix, and strengthens the immune system of people infected with the HIV virus. All yellow and red fruits and vegetables, and green leafy vegetables are good sources of this valuable nutrient.

TREAT YOURSELF TO A MANICURE

Graceful, silky hands and beautiful nails are much-prized, physical attributes. Supple hands and trim, healthy nails speak volumes about our state of health and personal grooming. Neglected hands, however, rather let the side down.

- Soak your hands in salt water for 15-20 minutes to relieve stiff, aching hands and reduce any swelling or puffiness.
- Polish your hands and nails (paying particular attention to the base, around the cuticle) using the *All-purpose Oatmeal Polisher* (see page 3). Regular polishing (exfoliation) reduces the intensity of pigmentation marks and normalizes the circulation.
- Now, rub hand cream into your knuckles and finger joints using small circular movements, followed by a pulling motion to ease the joints. Now use your thumbs to massage the backs of the hands upwards in the direction of the wrist to clear any congestion.

- File your nails using a large 'professional' emery board. Use the rough side to shorten and the smooth side to shape. Work in one direction rather than 'sawing' back and forth, as friction weakens the layer of the nails, causing them to split. If you want to shorten nails dramatically, clip across the top, then file the sides to desired shape.
- Remove all traces of varnish with acetone-free remover, which is much kinder to nails.
- Paint the nails using a clear base coat. Make sure the brush is not overloaded and that there is no varnish on the stem.
- Apply varnish using three strokes – side, middle, side – starting with the little finger and working towards the thumb.

FULL BODY MASSAGE

The rest of your evening is devoted to spoiling yourself with a full body massage. Should you wish, this would be a great time to involve your partner in your *Two Day Treat*.

With a partner these movements will feel sensual and relaxing, by yourself they will help you to tone, stimulate and cleanse your body. Regular massage not only improves your appearance but also promotes body-confidence and self-esteem.

Oil is used in these routines to encourage a smooth, rhythmic action and to avoid dragging the skin. Apply just enough to allow your fingers to glide smoothly over the skin.

- Almond oil – highly nutritious, versatile and easy to find.
- Olive oil – useful for excessively dry skin and lubricating larger areas of the body.
- Jojoba – a wonderful massage oil, especially for the face. Fairly costly, can be used on all skins. Mix with a workaday oil, such as sunflower, for massage purposes.
- Coconut oil – ideal for hair massage. The invisible coating left behind acts as a protective shield and locks moisture into the hair shaft. Available from chemists and Asian food stores, it is solid at room temperature.

GET READY

Bring a comfortable, upright chair into your chosen room and make sure you have a free surface for oils, cotton wool, a towel and maybe a comb. If you are doing this with a partner, it may be easier to lay towels down onto a bed.

Line up a bath mat to rest your feet on once they have been oiled. Fill a glass with water to sip away at. The room should be warm, as you will be uncovering different parts of your body while you work.

There is no need to place yourself in front of a mirror. The aim is to get your fingertips to connect with the nerve endings beneath the skin. If you are unable to see what you are doing, you are more likely to rely on your hands and your sense of touch will become more acute.

Sit well back in your chair with your bottom tucked under, tummy pulled in and shoulders relaxed and back. Do not slump in the middle, as this will prevent you from breathing well and so reduce the amount of oxygen available to your cells.

Check your position at the beginning of each routine and correct it if necessary. You will need to adjust your position slightly to carry out some procedures and to stand up to do others. Assume the sitting position unless stated otherwise.

Breathe slowly and deeply throughout and stop to take a few breaths in between routines. This will also help to keep your muscles relaxed.

THE SHOULDERS

Pour a few tablespoons of your massage oil into a bowl and apply a light film all over your shoulders and neck.

Front Shoulders

- ⊛ Position the first two fingers of each hand on your collarbones, at the point where they meet the breast bone. Press the balls of your fingers firmly into the flesh immediately beneath your collarbones and release.

- ⊛ Continue this movement as you progress out toward your shoulder joint. This should take about four moves. Return in the same manner to the breastbone. Repeat five times.

Back Shoulders

⊛ The trapezius muscle, a thick triangular-shaped muscle that lies behind your shoulder, is one of the most common sites for tension build up. Using the three middle fingers of one hand, massage thoroughly the part of the muscle located behind the opposite shoulder with small circular movements. Repeat on the other side. The greater the store of tension, the deeper you will need to work to release it. Increase pressure gradually.

⊛ Place your thumb in the hollow behind your collarbone and, using all four fingers, 'pinch' all over the muscle repeatedly. Repeat on other side.

⊛ The same vigorous pinching action, with your thumbs pointing downwards, can be used on the back of the neck moving up towards the hairline.

⊛ Continue for at least five minutes, switching between strokes and shoulders. Do not reduce the time spent on this routine.

THE ARMS

Remove any jewellery and apply almond oil all over your fingers, hands and arms. Do your left hand first if you are right-handed, and vice versa.

Hands

❀ With the thumb on top and your index finger in a supporting role, massage the balls of your fingers, your nails and your finger joints. Push your thumb along the furrows between the tendons that run down the back of your hand and glide it up towards the wrist to 'drain' the hand.

❀ You will need to work from the outside for the first three movements and from the thumb side for the last one.

❀ Pinch the web between each finger before you start each gliding action.

❀ While your thumb is manipulating the top of your hand, your fingers should be draining your palm in an upward motion. If they seem congested, apply extra pressure to the muscle pads on the outside of the hand.

Every time you use handcream give your hands a mini-therapy:

Rub cream into your knuckles and finger joints using small circular movements, followed by a pulling motion to ease the joints. Then use your thumbs to massage the backs of the hands upwards in the direction of the wrist.

Wrists

- Wrap the fingers of the working hand around the outside of the hand you are treating and massage all over the top side of your wrist joint, using small circular movements. Really roll your thumb around the bones on either side.

- Turn your wrist over and cradle it in the other hand while you do the underside.

Forearms

- Bend your arm and wrap your fingers around its underside, just above the wrist. Divide your arm into outer and inner 'tramlines' and use your thumb, pressing and gliding for short bursts and then releasing, to drain the tissue to the elbow in two sections.

- Your palm should not come into contact with your arm.

HEART 7

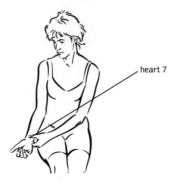

heart 7

Location: Draw an imaginary straight line on the palm, starting at the web of the third finger and little finger, and finishing at the wrist. It lies at the junction of this line and the wrist crease. Support the wrist with the fingers of the opposite hand, with the palm facing upwards, then locate the point with the thumb. Use your thumb to apply pressure for a minute.

Benefits: Calms the nervous system and relieves mental tension, anxiety and sleeplessness.

Elbows

- ⊛ Rest your hand on your abdomen and use the thumb and finger balls of the working hand to massage your elbow joint, making sure that you get into all the grooves.

Upper arms

- ⊛ Using all four fingers and your thumb, start on the outside of your upper arm at the elbow and work your way up to the shoulder, pinching your flesh as you go.
- ⊛ For the inside of your arm, use your thumb and fingers to reach round. Now repeat the movement. If your muscles are slack and underused, this may feel quite tender.

LARGE INTESTINE 11

Location: at the outer end of the skin crease, when the elbow is bent. Support the elbow in the fingers and palm of the opposite hand and apply deep pressure with the thumb.

Benefits: gently cleanses the digestive system and prevents/relieves constipation. Enhances the body's ability to assimilate nutrients from food, kick-starts the metabolism and improves body shape.

LEGS AND FEET

Lubricate the skin of your feet and legs with oil, being careful not to over-oil the feet. Cross one leg over the other so that you are sitting with one ankle resting on the other thigh. This enables you to reach your feet easily. Always start with your 'weaker' side first and work with the opposite hand unless otherwise specified.

Feet

- Massage all over your toes and toenails using your thumb and index finger. Pinch the web between you toes and, with the sole facing downwards, drain your feet in the same way you did your hands, using the thumb on the upper side and your three middle fingers on the sole.
- Now give the soles of your feet a good rub.

Ankle

- Adjust your position so that the outside of your foot is propped higher up your thigh, sole uppermost.
- Use the balls of your fingers to apply pressure to the different parts of your ankle, thumb on the inside and fingers on the outside.
- Work the area thoroughly, not forgetting the spot above the Achilles tendon.

Calves

The powerful muscles in the calves act as a pump helping circulation. This massage will help in this process.

- ⊛ The muscles of the calves are seldom relaxed since they are rarely off duty.
- ⊛ Slide your ankle a little way down the back of your thigh and massage the outside of the muscles using the forefingers, while your thumb does the inside.
- ⊛ The stroke is a deep pinching action.
- ⊛ Reverse the position of your fingers and thumb and repeat the movement.
- ⊛ Next, with the thumb and forefinger on either side of the shinbone, glide and drain upwards towards the knee.

NOTE: If you suffer from varicose veins, ignore the above instructions and palm the lower leg instead, using gentle sweeping strokes from ankle to knee.

Knees

- ⊛ Stand up and grasp lightly behind one knee with the fingers of both hands.
- ⊛ Position your thumbs on top and manipulate the joint both from front and back until it is thoroughly warmed.
- ⊛ Use your fingertips gently to ease the area around the kneecap.

Thighs

- Still in a standing position (possibly with one foot resting on the edge of a chair), massage all over your raised thigh by rotating your fingers and thumbs and applying a firm pressure.
- There are several large muscles in the upper legs, so you need to be systematic to make sure that you don't miss a section.
- Reduce the pressure over thread veins and go easier if you have fine skin.

Now repeat these routines on the other leg.

The Trunk

Warm the oil between your palms and apply a light covering all over your trunk. Stand with your feet shoulder-width apart, your bottom tucked under and your tummy pulled in. Your shoulders should be relaxed and back.

Bust

- There is no muscular tissue within the breasts themselves to keep them firm, but the neighbouring muscles help to provide support.
- Anchor your thumbs just inside your armpits and stimulate the area above the breasts (at the point where the bra and brastraps would meet) using deep pinches.
- Continue for a minute or so. Now, put one hand on top of one breast and use the other hand to massage underneath with large, deep, circular movements.
- Repeat 20 times on each side.

Stomach

- Check that you are in the correct standing position and that you have not allowed your abdominal muscles to collapse forward.
- Using firm pressure and a slow, circular motion, massage your abdomen with the palms of your hands for a couple of minutes, avoiding the area around the navel.
- Next grasp the flesh in big pinches and drain the side.

Hips and Buttocks

- Breathing slowly and deeply, tighten your buttock muscles and pinch firmly all over your hips and bottom, using your thumb and all four fingers. Repeat 30 times.

CELLULITE

One of the best ways to tackle cellulite is to get into the practice of dry skin brushing. Use a natural bristle brush before your bath or shower to boost circulation and aid the flow of the lymph.

Always brush in the direction of the heart and avoid broken or sore areas of skin.

Remember a healthy diet is crucial; plenty of fruit and vegetables, water and fresh juice. Cut back on wheat, dairy and refined products.

These approaches should be combined with exercise and massage.

11.00pm

Go to bed

Sunday morning

9am

BREAKFAST

Bharti 'bread' with a small helping of butter or
yogurt (non-dairy) with fresh fruit
A cup of Chai
A glass of freshly squeezed fruit juice

Extract the juice from fruit and vegetables to enjoy their revitalizing and regenerating properties in a different form. The nutrients in freshly squeezed juice require very little digesting, so are absorbed more quickly by the body. For the best results, drink the juice immediately, sipping it slowly and holding in your mouth for a few seconds before swallowing. A day or two on juice alone is a wonderful tonic for the system. Try your hand with oranges, grapes, papayas, mangoes and guavas (when in season), carrots, celery, grapes and ginger. Half a glass of freshly squeezed orange or carrot juice is an ideal way to start the day.

YOGA EXERCISES

This morning we are going to use yoga postures or *asanas* to build up a simple routine.

Asanas are an especially valuable form of exercise as they teach you to become aware of your breathing, as well as to resculpt and revitalize your body.

As with yesterday morning, go for a short walk to warm up your body before practising yoga.

THE CAT

- Kneel with legs slightly apart, hands on the floor under the shoulders. Try not to tense shoulders.
- Raising the head and breathing in, try to 'hollow' the spine as far as possible.
- Breathing out, lower the head as if to tuck the chin into the collar bone, and 'round' the spine as much as you can. In both movements, try to make the movement stretch all along the whole spine, not just one part of it. Return to starting position and repeat.

TREE

Vrksasana

- ⊛ Stand with one leg raised, foot against the opposite calf and hands on the hips. Practise concentrating on an unmoving spot and holding the balance on one leg for a few seconds.
- ⊛ Place the foot higher on the opposite leg with the heel against the groin or wherever you can manage.
- ⊛ Hands come up in a prayer position. Maintain balance for 10 seconds or as long as you can.
- ⊛ Remember: keep your eyes on an unmoving spot; hip bones and shoulders should be level; keep the standing leg strong and hold buttocks in.

STANDING HEAD TO KNEE POSE

Padahastasana

- ⊛ Stand up straight with your feet together. Keep the legs taut, and bend forwards from the hips *not the back.* Try to reach the floor with your fingers, or if you can not reach the floor, hold as far down the legs as you can. Do not tense the shoulders or pull, but feel the spine stretch out gently and easily.
- ⊛ Stretching the spine a little more, use the weight of the upper part of the body to stretch further forwards.
- ⊛ Holding on to the ankles, straighten the arms and look forward, concaving the spine. Stay for 10 seconds.
- ⊛ To come out, relax the back and arms and uncurl slowly one vertebra at a time, waist to neck, finally bring your head up.

WARRIOR POSE 1

Virabhadrasana 1

- Stand with your feet as far apart as you can manage. Turn the right foot in, left foot out, pivot round and place hands on the waist. The upper part of your body should now be facing directly forward.
- Bend the front leg, attempting a right angle with the floor. Keep the back leg straight and firm!
- Stretch the arms up above the head, palms pressed together, as straight as they will go. Look up at thumbs. Stay for 10 seconds
- Repeat on other side.

WARRIOR POSE 2

Virabhadrasana 2

- ⊛ Stand with your feet approximately 4ft apart. Turn your right foot out and your left foot slightly in (45º). Stretch out arms and fingers.
- ⊛ Turn your head to the right, keeping the chest facing forwards.
- ⊛ Begin to bend the right leg, and attempt to make a right angle with the floor. Sink into the posture.
- ⊛ Keep the shoulder and neck relaxed but imagine your hands being pulled in opposite directions.
- ⊛ Stay for 10 seconds and then repeat on your left side.

FORWARD BEND

Paschimottanasana

- Sit on the floor with legs straight out in front of you, toes up. Spread the flesh of your buttocks outwards to give yourself a relaxed 'seat' from which to bend forwards. Begin to bend slightly from the **pelvis and waist**, keeping the back straight.
- Using a belt or tie round the feet, gently guide the upper part of the body down over the legs.
- Bend as far as you can over the legs, without bending at the knees or rounding the shoulders and back. Try to relax the tummy onto thighs and the face onto the knees.
- Remember: The object is to stretch out the spine – not to bend forward just to get the head over the knees. Do not pull on the shoulders and try to keep the arms relaxed. Stay for 10 seconds
- Come out slowly, one vertebra at a time, finishing with the head.

SPINAL TWIST

Bharadvajasana

- Sit with the knees bent, and feet out to the left. Place left hand on the right knee and the right hand balancing the body on the floor at the back. Twist body gently.
- Reach the right hand round the back to hold the left elbow, thus bringing the body round and twisting the spine in a 'wringing out' movement. Try to keep both buttocks on the floor; if impossible, sit with a cushion under the raised buttock.
- Repeat on the other side.

SPIRITUAL RENEWAL

Breathing and meditation techniques are a crucial part of many spiritual disciplines. Breathing promotes healthy elimination of toxins from the body, promotes circulation, and increases energy. Meditation helps us to clear and relax our minds so that when we are active we can be more focused and effective. Meditation enhances our immune system, lowers blood pressure and combats stress. We may also experience a spiritual uplifting and a sense of calm.

BREATHING

These breath control exercises are part of yoga:

- ✺ Close your right nostril with your right thumb and inhale deeply through your left nostril. Close both nostrils and hold the air in your lungs for as long as is comfortable. Next, close your left nostril and exhale slowly through your right nostril. Keep your left nostril closed and inhale through your right nostril. Close both nostrils. Now slowly exhale through your left nostril. This in one cycle; do four more.
- ✺ Now adopt a comfortable sitting position, placing your hands on your knees and lowering your eyes. Inhale and exhale quickly and forcefully, like a pair of bellows. Start with one exhalation per second and gradually increase speed. Aim to complete one cycle of ten exhalations.

MEDITATION

- Remaining in your comfortable position, place your hands on your abdomen and slowly breathe in and out. Close your eyes. Concentrate on the breath; notice how the air flows in and out, and note the slight pause between each inhalation and exhalation. Feel your lungs as they fill and your abdomen as it rises and falls. Be conscious of the life force which is allowing you to breathe involuntarily.

- Keeping your eyes closed gradually bring your mind to someone who cares or cared for you deeply and unconditionally. Feel yourself surrounded by their love and support. Take in the love with every breath you take, expanding with it and embracing it. Know that you are worth it.

Ginger has a strong affinity with the mucous membranes that line the respiratory tract, and the ability to curb troublesome mucus production. The warming properties of ginger allow it to liquefy excess mucus, which keeps the passages of the nose and throat clear and helps indirectly conditions such as tinnitus. Ginger is also very effective in clearing the sinuses and even has the potential to reduce asthmatic tendencies. Try this tonic:

Peel a small ginger root, grate it and press out six or seven drops. Mix with hot water and ½ tsp honey.

IMPROVE YOUR POSTURE

Work on your standing and sitting posture and be aware when your back is arched or rounded in a slump. The idea is to preserve the gentle, natural curves in your spine.

Good posture pivots on the correct pelvic tilt because, when the pelvis is balanced, the spine is subject to minimum stress. It is achieved by tucking your bottom under your spine.

When you are sitting, your upper back should be straight and your lower back angled slightly forwards. A small cushion slipped into the small of your back may help to balance your pelvis.

POSTURAL EXERCISE

Stand squarely on the outside of your feet and imagine that there are roots descending from your heels deep into the ground. Imagine, too, that there is a tail attached to your tailbone, which pulls down on the end of the spine and encourages it to sink with the force of gravity. At the same time, visualize a piece of string extending upwards from the crown of your head, stretching your spine and making you taller and leaner. This is the 'plumb line' which travels down the spine through the pelvis – the body's centre of gravity – towards the ground.

1.00pm

LUNCH

Bharti's 'Bread'
Bharti's Special Dal
Tomato and Cucumber Raita

TOMATO AND CUCUMBER RAITA

This cooling flavour of yogurt goes well with many foods.
Made ahead and chilled, this simple salad is a wonderful
accompaniment to peppery curry dishes and dals.

Ingredients

2 ripe, medium tomatoes, skinned and
chopped (plum tomatoes are best)
$^1/_2$ large cucumber, peeled and shredded
1 cup of yogurt (Greek-style yogurt gives
excellent results)
1 tsp ground cumin
pinch of asafoetida (optional)
salt and black pepper
fresh mint, chopped, to garnish

Asafoetida (heeng) is used in several systems of healing. It subdues wind and the nasal mucus, and is said to increase the appetite. It aids gastric processes, strengthens the heart and regulates the menstrual cycle. It is also a tonic for the liver and spleen, and can be used in the treatment of rheumatism, deafness, paralysis and eye disease. In other words, don't let its smell put you off. A tiny amount of heeng in your food each day helps you stay young.

1 Prepare the tomatoes and cucumbers and allow them to drain in a sieve to remove excess moisture.
2 In a bowl, combine the yogurt and spices. Stir well.
3 Add drained vegetables to the mixture, and gently combine by turning over 2 or 3 times with a wooden spoon.
4 Refrigerate for at least 2 hours before serving. Garnish with chopped mint.

Sunday afternoon

REFLEXOLOGY

Sunday afternoon is an excellent time to pamper your often neglected feet. Try out the ancient Chinese massage technique of reflexology and treat yourself to a pedicure.

Reflexology is based on the principle that nerve centres in the feet are directly connected to other parts of the body. Massaging these nerve centres – known as reflexes – can pinpoint problems in various organs. Working on these tender spots, with tiny movements, stimulates the nerves that connect to the problem organs.

Begin on the weakest foot, the one that feels more tender to the touch and remember that a foot massage should not stop at the feet; always extend the work up the ankle.

The reflexology zones:

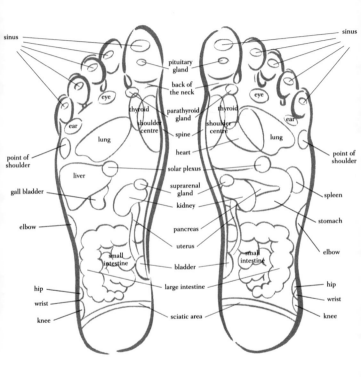

1 Press on these three points (on the opposite page) and move your fingers upwards, maintaining a deep pressure to encourage improved circulation.

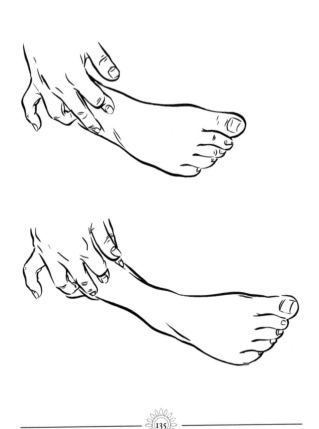

2 The area surrounding the inner ankle bone is very important. Make deep finger ball pressure (see pg 54) to stimulate the spleen and kidney meridians, which are very important points in Chinese medicine. Applying acupressure here leads to detoxification, helps to remove waste products, gives good hormonal balance, and allows the tissues to work better.

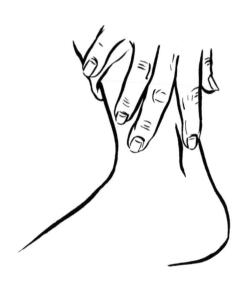

3 If the inside of the leg is sensitive, keep working, but decrease the pressure as you move your fingers up the leg to a point four fingers widths above the tip of the ankle bone. Be careful to avoid bruising yourself. Even working gently on the thinner skin on this very powerful acupoint is beneficial, as it is the meeting point of the spleen, liver and kidney meridians.

4 The base of the fleshy part of the underside of your foot is a good acupressure pump and is found in the depression just below the ball of the foot. Pressing deeply for up to a minute, and letting go several times helps to invigorate the circulation, promotes vitality, helps to balance blood pressure, and is a good treatment for older people as it increases blood flow to all areas.

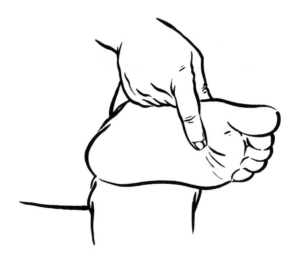

5 This is spleen 6, in Chinese medicine it is recognized as the strongest point for controlling the hormones. To find it, mark out your four fingers from the ankle bone as a guide. Press your thumb into the point using deep pressure before letting go. Repeat this several times. Working in the outside of the ankle can also benefit the ovaries.

(NOT to be used when pregnant.)

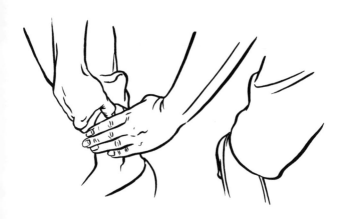

6 The area surrounding the bone is very important, and can help to reduce high blood pressure. Use concentrated deep finger ball pressure.

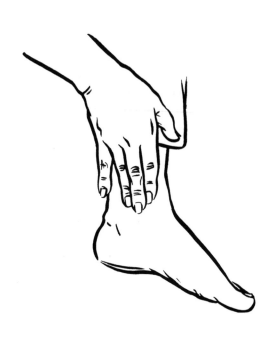

7 These points are very important for blood pressure. Press with quite a deep pressure, and then drag your fingers away to give a boost to your circulation. Working on the front of the foot also improves liver function and boosts the immune system. Pull your fingers firmly along the top of the foot to intercept the nerve junction. Repeat the process to relieve the effects of stress and toxins on the body, and regulate blood pressure.

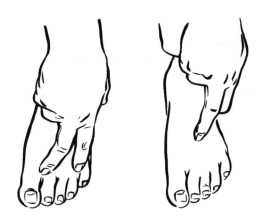

LOOKING AFTER
YOUR FEET

'Out of sight – out of mind' seems to best describe our relationship with our feet, this is a shame as a little effort can transform them into a stunning feature – especially for the summer!

HOME PEDICURE

- Soak your feet in a salt bath for 20 minutes to improve circulation and control bacteria.
- Polish using the *All-Purpose Oatmeal Polisher*. Concentrate on hard bony areas, such as the heel and ball of the foot. Really leathery patches of hard skin may also be tackled with a pumice stone.
- Stimulate the circulation to the small joints in the toes by massaging each of your toes between your index finger and thumb. Continue for one or two minutes per toe.
- Gently push your cuticles back with a flannel, again using small circular movements. Repeat these steps on the other side.

- ⊛ Dry your feet thoroughly.
- ⊛ Follow up with a good foot cream (ideally with anti-bacterial and anti-fungal properties) or almond oil, massaged into the whole foot, concentrating on the soles.
- ⊛ Clip and file the nails squarely, in line with the end of the toes, so that the growth does not head into the surrounding soft tissue. File them regularly to avoid jagged edges as if you catch the nail it can lift it and cause permanent damage to the bed.
- ⊛ Paint with a clear base coat.

RELAX, RENEW, REVIVE!

At the Bharti Vyas Holistic Therapy & Beauty Centre:

Beauty on the outside ... begins on the inside.

To contact Bharti Vyas or to find out more about Bharti Vyas Beauty Products you can write to:

Bharti Vyas Holistic Therapy & Beauty Centre
24 Chiltern Street
London
W1M 1PF

Tel: 0207 486 7910

The centre also has a website at www.bharti-vyas.co.uk or you can email your questions to Bharti at bhartivyas@aol.com.